CAN SEX IMPROVE YOUR GOLF?

...AND CAN GOLF IMPROVE YOUR SEX?

BY
TONI GOFFE

First published in Great Britain by
Pendulum Gallery Press
56 Ackender Road, Alton, Hants GU34 1JS

© TONI GOFFE 1992

CAN SEX IMPROVE YOUR GOLF?
ISBN 0-948912-18-9

REPRINTED 1992, 1993

PRINTED IN GREAT BRITAIN BY
UNWIN BROTHERS LTD, OLD WOKING, SURREY

'THERE'S MORE TO HITTING THIS BALL THAN
I FIRST THOUGHT....'

'HI, I'M THE GOLF PROFESSIONAL AND THIS IS ALICE THE OTHER PROFESSIONAL!...'

'DON'T WASTE YOUR TIME, HE'S WELL UNDER PAR TODAY....'

"WOULD YOU MIND IF I FELT YOUR GRIP?"

'OUR GOLF CARTS RUN ON ELECTRICITY, MR SMITH,
SO WE CAN'T BE OUT OF PETROL...'

' HA, HA, BALL COMPRESSION IN THE SWEET SPOT EH, FRANK?!'

'THIS IS AN EQUAL OPPORTUNITY GOLF CLUB MR STEWART...'

'CAN WE BORROW A WEDGE, WE KEEP SLIPPING DOWN THIS BANK .....'

' AH, YOU MUST BE THE NEW HAZARD EVERYONE'S
TALKING ABOUT....

' NINE IRON .!! '

'FOR HEAVEN'S SAKE JACK, LOST IS LOST, PLAY ANOTHER ONE ....'

" I DON'T KNOW WHY WE DIDN'T TRY
THESE MIXED FOURSOMES BEFORE...."

'OH! NO! THE WIFE'S DOING HER BLOODY
RAIN-DANCE AGAIN....

'WELL MISS SMYTHE WHAT IS IT TO BE, THE FIRST TEE, OR THE HOTEL SPLENDIDE?....'

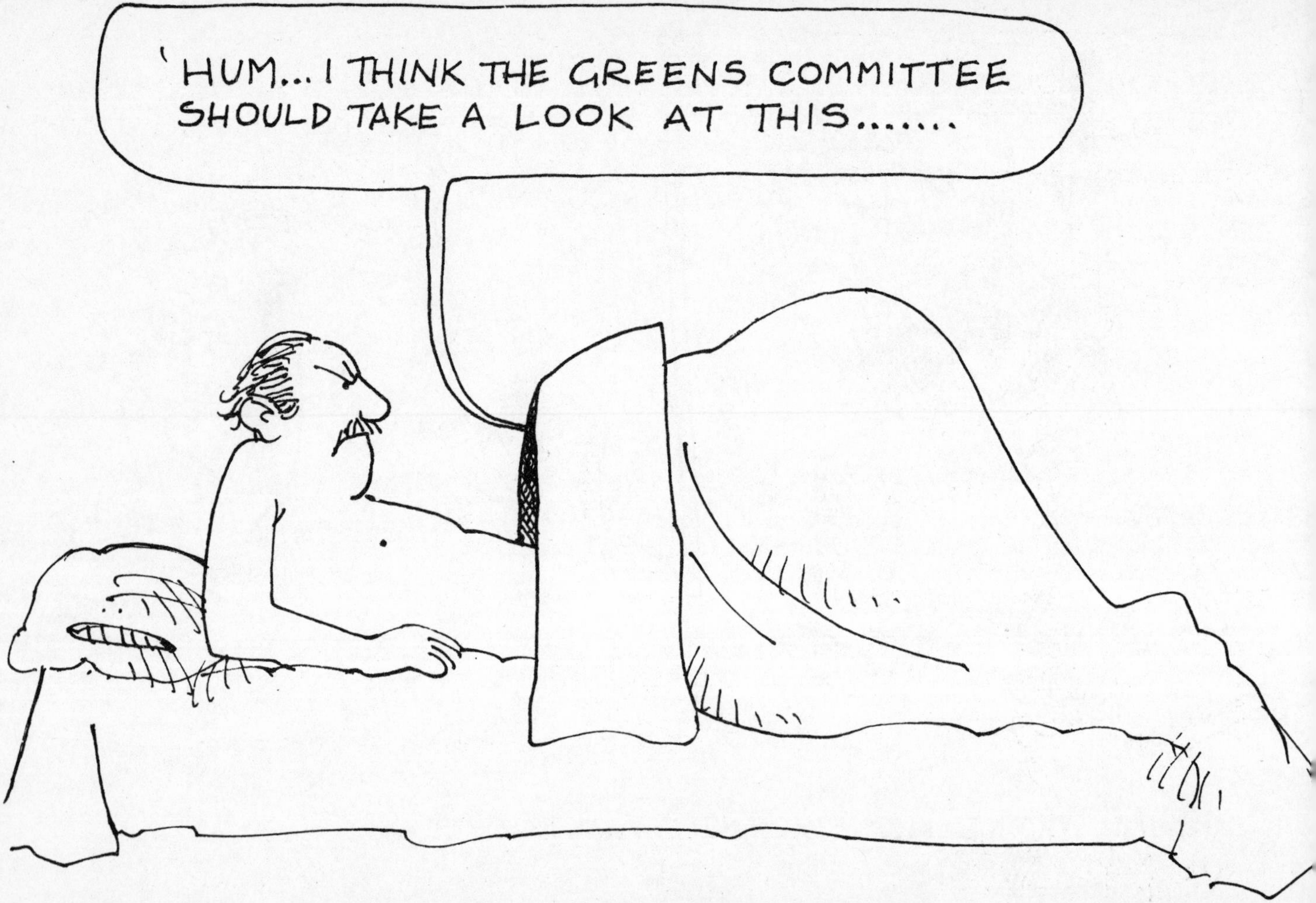
HUM... I THINK THE GREENS COMMITTEE SHOULD TAKE A LOOK AT THIS......

'OH DEAR, IT LOOKS LIKE YOUR WIFE'S GOING TO BE A REAL GOLF WIDOW....'

'PLEASE CAN RANDY COME OUT TO PLAY?'

'OH NO! IT'S MY HUSBAND! HE MUST HAVE
GIVEN UP GOLF — AGAIN!!...'

'I'VE COME TO COLLECT YOUR MEMBERSHIP FEES...'

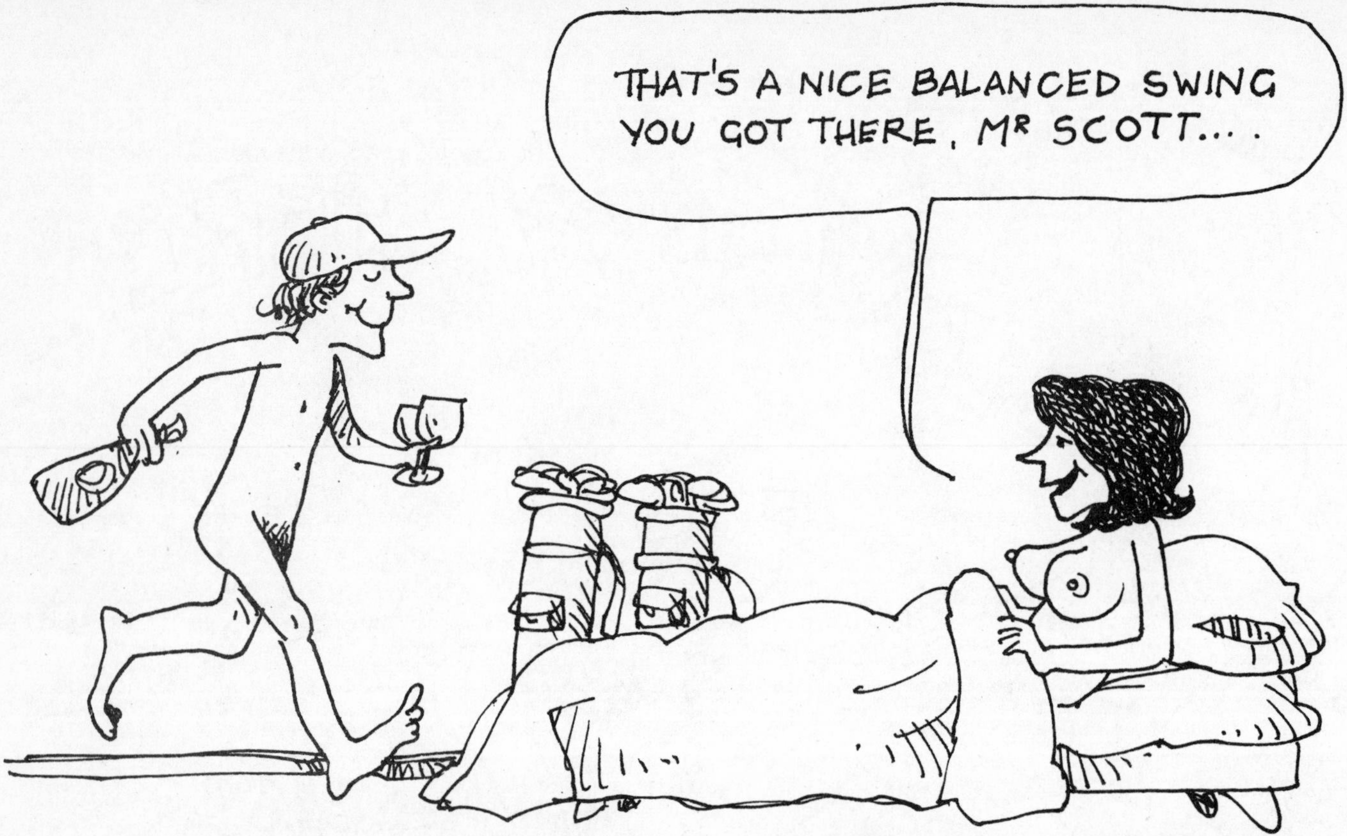
THAT'S A NICE BALANCED SWING YOU GOT THERE, MR SCOTT....